Burgess

EDUCATION SERIES

Consulting Editor — LAURENCE S. FLAUM

PHOTOSITUATIONS
a technique for teaching

by

DAVID POTTER
Professor of Speech
Southern Illinois University

J. JOEL MOSS
Professor of Family Life Education
Brigham Young University

HERBERT F. A. SMITH
Professor of Education
Southern Illinois University

Burgess Publishing Company
426 South 6th Street • Minneapolis 15, Minnesota

Contents

Introduction

Some forty years ago, H. G. Wells observed prophetically that the world was witnessing a race between education and annihilation. Today many social critics believe that the contest is entering the homestretch--with education lagging far behind. Little wonder that the proponents of education are so concerned about the methods of training used by their champion, the teacher, as he courts ever-increasing responsibility and undergoes ever-changing adjustment.

In the pages that follow we are offering materials and proposing a methodology which may help the teacher and the student gain the increased sensitivity, the keener perceptivity, the deeper understanding, the more valid judgment, and the more effective communicative skills so necessary for his survival and ours. We do not believe that what we have assembled should be considered as the sole means by and through which any particular course should be taught. But, we do believe that these materials and the proposed methodology will augment the lecture, the verbal or written case study, the film, and the textbook. We believe, too, that these materials and this methodology will furnish a mainspring of active and responsible discussion.

I. Our Materials

The basis for this workbook is a collection of twenty-four photographs representing a wide sampling of incidents in the school and the community in which the teacher operates as a guide, a disciplinarian, a source of information and service, and a symbol of propriety. Although the majority of the pictures appear to be teacher-training oriented, it is apparent that a number of them are pertinent to such other areas concerned with human interaction as Guidance, Educational Psychology, Adolescent Psychology, Sociology of Child Development, Child Development, Methods of Teaching, Group Dynamics, Social Work, and Speech (especially Discussion and Speech for the Classroom Teacher).

Preceding each group of photographed situations are brief introductions and following each situation, we hope, tantalizing questions. The introductions are intended to give some structuring to the situation or situations by involving a pertinent issue in teacher training. Such structuring may help focus student attention toward certain pedagogical principles while leaving room for alternative perceptions and judgments. The questions are intended to draw out a "let us locate and attack this problem together" rather than the common "let me tell you" approach in education.

II. Our Procedures

Let us first assume we all realize that there is no one proper way to utilize our pictures. An assumption to the contrary is no more warranted than a conclusion that our sampling of situations represents all possible situations. Obviously, the course in which the pictures will be used as well as the experience and inclinations of the individual instructor and the abilities and maturity of the individuals in his class will have considerable bearing upon methods of utilization and the time spent on them. It is quite possible that some instructors will simply announce that class discussion will center on, say, picture seven. And at class time, discussion will proceed as smoothly and penetrate as deeply as it frequently does where the case method is well utilized. But many of us and most of our students will require some procedural guidance. Let us, then, offer several general suggestions and follow this with specific procedures which may be applied whether the workbook is used as the main or as a supplementary vehicle of instruction.

If you have already thumbed through the contents of this workbook, you have discovered that the brief introductions to the various groupings of pictures have been designed to call attention to certain common facets of teacher experiences. These groupings are not sacrosanct! They seemed convenient to us. Similarly, the questions following each group of pictures while not worded identically, can be used interchangeably. Basically they ask: (1) What does the observer see? (2) What evidence appears to support such perception? (3) What are the likely outcomes of such action in terms of the principles which are pertinent? (4) What are the alternative solutions or possibilities for explaining and resolving these outcomes? By requesting that each student write out his considered answers to the questions, we are attempting to guard against the possible tyranny of the discussion group. So frequently the prevailing opinion of the majority eradicates keen but unpopular perceptions and good but unrepresentative conclusions. When the individual has had less time to formulate his opinions, he is less likely to defend them. These answers, also, can be used at a later point in the course to indicate how the individual has changed his mind or his thinking as a consequence of discussion or further study.

A. A Procedural Approach

1. We suggest that it might be useful to open the course with a device aimed at pointing up the inherent possibilities for error as individuals perceive and report action. We frequently employ an adaptation of the now classic experiment described by Professors Allport and Postman in their "Basic Psychology of Rumor". A slide made of their subway train incident is projected so that everyone in the class can see it except members of a group of six or seven "volunteers". One of the "volunteers" is called into the room and shown the slide or told what the picture contains. He then relates what he has seen or heard to another subject who has been asked to

enter the room. This procedure is repeated until each of the "volunteers" has gone through the hear-and-report sequence. Then everyone is shown the slide and the final "rumor" is compared with the actual incident. The consequence is hilarity, a realization of human frailty, and a necessary introduction to the importance of adequate perception and accurate reporting in the process of locating and solving difficulties. [1]

2. We now open the classroom discussion of an assigned photosituation by posing to the group the first question the students have already "answered" on the question sheets. If the particular lead question does not function adequately as a discussion "primer", we might ask the students to describe exactly what they detect in the situation frozen by the camera, and then indicate the supporting clues in movement, dress, etc. It is worth observing at this point that, important as is the picture to the learning situation, even more important is what the observer sees, how he reports it, what reasoning processes he employs, and what sensitivity to human relations he demonstrates.

3. If the instructor observes that emotional reactions need unlocking and mental processes require unjamming, he may alleviate much of the difficulty and encourage depth of understanding by introducing role playing. Simply stated, this involves requesting students to assume the roles of key individuals in the photosituation. After the acting has progressed sufficiently to indicate the point or points we wish to emphasize, we stop the players and pose our questions: "What was your reaction as . . . ?" What were you thinking as . . . ?" Selecting the actors, of course, is not a hit-or-miss affair. Some students find it impossible to unlock their inhibitions even when they are playing another role. But not at all strangely, we have discovered that elementary education majors have few overwhelming inhibitions while facing a class. A caution--be careful to stop the playing after the point to be emphasized has been reached. There seems to be an infectious element to role playing. The technique can run off with the instructor's agenda! [2]

4. Sometimes, as a consequence of the role playing or the preliminary search for information contained in the photosituation, the students discover that they do not have enough information upon which to predict a satisfactory course of action or the probability of a solution's being accepted by the individuals involved. When such an impasse is reached, we suggest that the instructor borrow from a variation of the case method promulgated by the Pigors. [3]

[1] See Gordon W. Allport and Leo F. Postman, "The Basic Psychology of Rumor", reprinted in Theodore M. Newcomb and Eugene L. Hartley, editors, Readings in Social Psychology, New York: Henry Holt and Company, 1948, 547-558; and Irving J. Lee and Laura L. Lee, Handling Barriers in Communication, New York: Harper & Brothers, 1957, 64-70.

[2] There is an abundance of literature dealing with role playing. A good starting point might be David Potter and Martin P. Andersen, Discussion: A Guide to Effective Practice, Belmont, California: Wadsworth Publishing Company, 1963.

[3] See Paul Pigors and Faith Pigors, The Incident Process: Case Studies in Management, Washington, D. C.: Bureau of National Affairs, 1935; and "The Incident Process . . . ," Management Methods, February, 1956, 15-20.

One such procedure might involve assigning to one or two of the keener students the difficult but rewarding task of filling in the specific background for the particular incident. The search for and writing up of this background is difficult and time consuming because it requires not only knowledge of people and their emotional entanglements but also the twin responsibilities of knowing where and how to tap reliable sources and having the creative ability to see the nature of the sequence of which the incident is only a part. It is rewarding, if accomplished successfully, because it engenders good research and analytical habits and the feeling of confidence so necessary to the success of a beginning teacher. Few of our young teachers know how to find and organize the data they need in order to see the situation in its entirety. Seldom can they face a crisis armed only with a carefully documented case study or a set of notes dealing with the solving of that specific problem! Should the classroom assignment end in failure, the result is not nearly so painful as failure in the real situation. In our classroom the damage is limited to the temporary blow to pride and point average; and in our classroom there should be a chance to recoup without risk to one's academic future.

5. When case writers have been appointed and their written assignment has been completed, the class as a whole or the section of the class discussing a particular incident must then accept the responsibility for drawing from the case writers the information considered necessary for further prognosis. Again students discover the need for considerable insight and, during the first few discussions, some assistance from the instructor.

6. Once the group has the information it believes it needs, it turns its attention to discussion--usually attempting to resolve the difficulties indicated by prior analysis or by the questioning of the case writers. Occasionally, or if the class in question is a speech class, the instructor might follow a pattern suggested by the Pigors and have subgroups arrive at independent conclusions which, in turn, are upheld in prepared argumentative speeches by representatives of the subgroups. Parliamentary sessions, finally, could resolve the majority's choice of solution.

7. Following the close of the discussion and the reaching of a conclusion or conclusions, the instructor might end a particular assignment by calling for an evaluatory "post-mortem" of the entire discussion. This evaluation might be furnished by an "expert", by a committee of observers appointed prior to the outset of the discussion, or by the discussants themselves. Then, the evaluation digested, the class may turn to the next photographed situation or to another phase of course work, while the instructor, if he is like us, vows that in future class discussions he will remain in the background, and if he does participate at all it will usually be as a catalyst, perhaps as a guide, and occasionally as a devil's advocate. [4]

[4]Familiarity with the following volumes will assist an instructor who takes the vow: Kenneth R. Andrews, editor, The Case Method of Teaching Human Relations and Administration, Cambridge: Harvard University Press, 1956; Dean C. Barnlund and Franklyn S. Haiman, The Dynamics of Discussion, Boston: Houghton Mifflin, 1960; Richard Beckhard, How to Plan and Conduct Workshops and Conferences, New York: Association Press, 1956; Charles H. Clark, Brainstorming, New York: Doubleday and Company, 1958; Thomas Gordon, Group-Centered Leadership, Boston: Houghton Mifflin, 1955; Norman R. F. Maier, Principles of Human Relations,

B. A Second Procedural Approach

Frequently we adopt a simple procedure based upon the buzz session technique or, as it is also called, the discussion cluster or Phillips 66.[5] To illustrate, let us assume that our class has 32 students, that we are studying photosituation A--which follows--that we have gone through the "Rumor Clinic", and that the question before the class is "What illustrations of good or poor practice do you perceive in this picture?" Each student has been given five or ten minutes to write his observations and reactions to the clues presented. The instructor opens the discussion.

TEACHER: David, what do you see? Please identify the most significant clue which you have observed.

DAVID: I think the deplorable physical setup is most important. The light is bad and . . . .

TEACHER: Let's make a note of physical condition. (He writes "physical condition" on the blackboard.) Now let us consider another angle. Stephen, what do you see?

STEPHEN: I agree with David. The room is very poor but the presence of the janitor seems to be a disturbing element too.

TEACHER: Right. We'll add the janitor. (Writes "janitor's presence" on the board.) Now, Judy, do you have anything to add?

JUDY: Yes. The blackboard is inadequate and not well used.

TEACHER: Good. Number three will be "blackboard use". Does anyone else detect a clue to a situation or condition he would like to add to the list? Pat?

PAT: I think the pupils are holding a conversation of their own while the teacher is pointing to things on the board. You probably can say that his control is weak.

TEACHER: Would "class control" fit?

PAT: Yes, that would express what I mean.

New York: John Wiley & Sons, 1952; Matthew B. Miles, Learning to Work in Groups, New York: Bureau of Publications, Teachers College, Columbia University, 1959; William M. Sattler and N. Edd Miller, Discussion and Conference, New York: Prentice-Hall, 1954; Harold P. Zelko, Successful Conference and Discussion Techniques, New York; McGraw-Hill, 1957; Nathaniel Cantor; The Teaching-Learning Process, New York: Dryden Press, 1953; Clark E. Moustakas, The Alive and Growing Teacher, New York: Philosophical Library, 1959; Adult Education Association of the U.S.A., Leadership Pamphlet #1, How to Lead Discussions, #6, How to Use Role Playing, and #4, Understanding How Groups Work, 743 North Wabash Avenue, Chicago, 1956; Warren H. Schmidt and Paul C. Buchanan, Techniques That Produce Teamwork, New London, Conn.: Arthur C. Croft Publs., 1954; David Potter and Martin P. Andersen, Discussion: A Guide to Effective Practice, Belmont, California: Wadsworth Publishing Company, 1963.

[5] For a detailed description of this technique see Potter and Andersen, op.cit., pp.

Figure 1

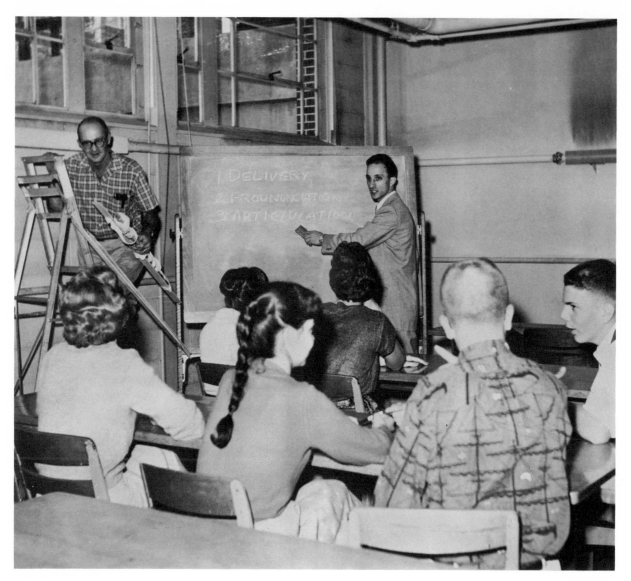

(Teacher writes "class control" on the board.)

TEACHER: We have identified four aspects of the teaching situation as pictured in this frozen incident. Each of these is important enough to warrant some discussion. In each case, discussion should lead to some answers for the questions which follow the picture. Note those especially which deal with generalizations.

Will each of you who identified a factor act as a leader of a small group please? You can use each corner of the room with your chairs in circles if you wish. (A minute is used here to divide the class according to individual choices of subject.)

(There is nothing sacred about dividing the class into four groups, of course. Three or six might fit the situation better. We will visit the group which has David as chairman. There are eight students in it.)

DAVID: Our topic is the deplorable conditions under which this man is trying to teach. It seems exaggerated somewhat but we had classes in basement rooms not much better when I was in high school. Let's look at these questions. (Reading.) What principles of teaching are violated? What would you do to ameliorate the situation? What generalizations concerning teaching would you formulate from your thinking? (Stops reading.) Gloria, would you like to lead off?

GLORIA: I think the first principle I see violated is that of lighting. There must be a terrible glare coming from those unshaded windows so high up. To look at the board, some of the children must face them directly.

DOROTHY: I think the aesthetic side of the picture bothers me most. Boys and girls should not spend their time looking at pipes and things. Those pipes probably drip in hot weather and get the teacher and everybody wet. I wouldn't teach in a place like that!

(David gets the group back to business after some general comments about Dorothy's attitude.)

DAVID: Joe, do you have something to say?

JOE: Yes. The teacher could ameliorate the situation as the book puts it by moving the board to the other side of the room so that the light is better. He could also change the seating so that the pupils have their backs to the light. Of course then he would have to face the light and get a headache; but, after all, he is the teacher.

DOROTHY: I think it is an awful place whatever he does.

JOE: He could ask the janitor to do his job some other time. I think Stephen's group will get into that.

(After some more discussion involving heat, types of seating, the desirable place for the teacher's desk and so on, the chairman tries to tie the discussion together.)

DAVID: We have done a lot of talking and some thinking. Let's attempt to summarize it. Gloria, how would you generalize what you said?

GLORIA: I have written it down. "Each pupil should have light good enough for him to do his work without strain. Deep shadows and glare are undesirable."

DAVID: O. K. Dorothy, have you one?

DOROTHY: Yes. Very definitely. "Each pupil deserves a pleasant place in which to work."

DAVID: That leaves the word "pleasant" to be interpreted, but let that go and we'll see if anyone picks it up. Joe, what about what you said?

JOE: "The teacher is responsible to use his classroom and the materials in it so that the pupils have the optimum use of it." That's wordy, I know, but I want to get in the whole idea.

8

DAVID: Is there anything else? Pat?

PAT: I think we could trespass on the control group a little. The physical aspect is important to control. Let's say this: "The type of seating used in a class and the manner in which it is used are important factors in maintaining good discipline."

DAVID: Shall we accept that? Gloria, you write well on the board. Will you write our generalizations on the first section so that we can all see them when the class gets back together? Thank you.

(We will now join Judy's group since it seems they must subsist on thinner fare than the others.)

JUDY: Well, if I hadn't said so much I wouldn't be doing this chairmanship bit. But I always was bothered by teachers who used dirty boards and wrote too badly for anyone to read what they wrote. So let's face these questions and see what we can do.

(They have the same questions as David's group.)

JUDY: Wesley, can you start?

WESLEY: Yes. The first thing is that "pronunciation" and "articulation" are misspelled. This is pretty bad. If we can't spell, we can look words up beforehand. I think his lesson planning is inadequate.

JUDY: That is a good point. Bill?

BILL: It's a pretty crumby blackboard in the first place and it's dirty in the second place. Of course, it must be hard to keep such a small board clean.

JUDY: Yes, but the board size is the school board's fault, not the teacher's. Carol?

CAROL: The teacher is standing the wrong way. He should have a pointer and stand to our right of the board and point with his right hand. Perhaps the boy talking at the end of the table would be more attentive if he could see what is going on.

(As with the other group, the conversation goes along for ten or fifteen minutes with the talk about quality of writing, the use of printing, blackboard cleaning methods, and so on. Judy calls the group to order.)

JUDY: Have any of you nice clean statements of the generalizations we have reached?

CAROL: I have jotted down what I have summed up. Here it is: "The teacher stands away from the blackboard when he is finished writing on it so that each pupil has a clear view."

WESLEY: Mine goes like this: "The correct spelling and pronunciation of all words to be used in a lesson must be determined at the planning stage of the lesson and cannot be left to chance."

BILL: I would like to put my point like this: "Each classroom should have adequate boards of good quality. The teacher has the responsibility of keeping the surface clean and of manipulating the lighting system so that there is no glare."

JUDY: You have about three generalizations there, but we can let the whole class deal with that. Carol, you told us what the teacher should do with the board, so will you please write these statements so that all can see them?

CAROL: I guess I'm stuck with it.

JUDY: That's right, you are. Thanks for doing it.

As a result of this work, the teacher has four lists of statements, purported to be generalizations, on the board. The class as a whole deals with each one, accepting or rejecting it, or, more likely, modifying it. Eventually each member of the class has in his notes a series of generalizations which reflect the thinking of his teacher, his classmates, and himself.

C. Evaluation Forms

Following discussion of each photosituation and the generalizations which stem from our analysis of the picture, we devote at least one class session to an evaluation of both the small group and the general class discussion. Usually, we open with a mild critique by the instructor or "expert" utilizing as guidelines the questions on the form titled General Effectiveness of Discussion.

After the first critique, we encourage more specific evaluation of individual performance. The form titled Effectiveness of Individual Participation has been utilized with considerable success by student evaluators, particularly when a body of critics is set up as a panel.

In addition to requiring "expert" and student evaluation, usually in panel form, we ask each member of the small group (buzz, cluster, or 66) to fill out a Group Reaction Sheet which indicates to the instructor how the various group members feel about the group and its accomplishments. A careful analysis of this sheet by the instructor enables him to modify his group structures and his procedures when necessary.

General Effectiveness of Discussion

Evaluator:

Group:

Date:

1. What is your over-all estimate of the effectiveness of the discussion?

2. What did you like most?

3. What did you like least?

4. What changes would you suggest to the group which might improve their next discussion?

5. What comments would you make to specific members of the group?

Effectiveness of Individual Participation

Observer:

Discussant:

Date:

1. How observant did the discussant appear to be?

2. What analytical skills did he demonstrate?

3. How well did he communicate?

4. What were his major contributions (giving and testing information and ideas, clarifying or seeking clarification, relieving tension, etc.) to the discussion?

5. In what ways did he aid in building an atmosphere conducive to good discussion (accepting ideas, relieving tension, contributing to group morale, etc.)?

6. What changes in attitude and what skills would have enhanced his value to his group or to the entire class?

Effectiveness of Individual Participation

Observer:

Discussant:

Date:

1. How observant did the discussant appear to be?

2. What analytical skills did he demonstrate?

3. How well did he communicate?

4. What were his major contributions (giving and testing information and ideas, clarifying or seeking clarification, relieving tension, etc.) to the discussion?

5. In what ways did he aid in building an atmosphere conducive to good discussion (accepting ideas, relieving tension, contributing to group morale, etc.)?

6. What changes in attitude and what skills would have enhanced his value to his group or to the entire class?

Effectiveness of Individual Participation

Observer:

Discussant:

Date:

1. How observant did the discussant appear to be?

2. What analytical skills did he demonstrate?

3. How well did he communicate?

4. What were his major contributions (giving and testing information and ideas, clarifying or seeking clarification, relieving tension, etc.) to the discussion?

5. In what ways did he aid in building an atmosphere conducive to good discussion (accepting ideas, relieving tension, contributing to group morale, etc.)?

6. What changes in attitude and what skills would have enhanced his value to his group or to the entire class?

Effectiveness of Individual Participation

Observer:

Discussant:

Date:

1. How observant did the discussant appear to be?

2. What analytical skills did he demonstrate?

3. How well did he communicate?

4. What were his major contributions (giving and testing information and ideas, clarifying or seeking clarification, relieving tension, etc.) to the discussion?

5. In what ways did he aid in building an atmosphere conducive to good discussion (accepting ideas, relieving tension, contributing to group morale, etc.)?

6. What changes in attitude and what skills would have enhanced his value to his group or to the entire class?

Effectiveness of Individual Participation

Observer:

Discussant:

Date:

1. How observant did the discussant appear to be?

2. What analytical skills did he demonstrate?

3. How well did he communicate?

4. What were his major contributions (giving and testing information and ideas, clarifying or seeking clarification, relieving tension, etc.) to the discussion?

5. In what ways did he aid in building an atmosphere conducive to good discussion (accepting ideas, relieving tension, contributing to group morale, etc.)?

6. What changes in attitude and what skills would have enhanced his value to his group or to the entire class?

Group Reaction Sheet

Group:

Date:

(Please check the point on each scale that represents your considered opinion. If you wish to clarify or explain your decision, please do so briefly in the space indicated by "Explanation". Do not sign your name.)

1. Are you satisfied with the conclusions (if any) reached in the discussion?

    VERY   MODERATELY   NOT AT ALL

    Explanation:

2. Were the attitudes of your fellow discussants conducive to cooperative action?

    VERY   MODERATELY   NOT AT ALL

    Explanation:

3. Did the group adopt and follow an orderly or systematic approach toward the solving of the problem confronting it?

    TOO MUCH SO VERY MUCH SO SOMEWHAT NOT AT ALL

    Explanation:

4. As a consequence of the discussion, have you gained any new insights or new and useful information and understanding?

    A GREAT DEAL   SOME   VERY LITTLE

    Explanation:

5. Were you given opportunities to express your opinions and material?

    OFTEN   OCCASIONALLY   INFREQUENTLY

    Explanation:

6. Would you suggest any changes in the leadership of the discussion?

    MANY   A FEW   NONE AT ALL

    Explanation:

7. Which of the following changes would benefit the group? (Check as many as you wish.)

    _____ a. Better statement of questions to be explored.
    _____ b. Better individual preparation.
    _____ c. More responsible leadership.
    _____ d. More carefully planned agenda.
    _____ e. More democratic leadership.
    _____ f. More consideration for members of the group.
    _____ g. A greater sharing of leadership responsibilities.
    _____ h. A different procedure.
    _____ i. A friendlier atmosphere.
    _____ j. Consideration of different topics for discussion.
    _____ k. A more valid approach to discussion.
    _____ l. A change in the behavior of the instructor.

    Explanation:

Group Reaction Sheet

Group:

Date:

(Please check the point on each scale that represents your considered opinion. If you wish to clarify or explain your decision, please do so briefly in the space indicated by "Explanation". Do not sign your name.)

1. Are you satisfied with the conclusions (if any) reached in the discussion?

   VERY   MODERATELY   NOT AT ALL

   Explanation:

2. Were the attitudes of your fellow discussants conducive to cooperative action?

   VERY   MODERATELY   NOT AT ALL

   Explanation:

3. Did the group adopt and follow an orderly or systematic approach toward the solving of the problem confronting it?

   TOO MUCH SO   VERY MUCH SO   SOMEWHAT   NOT AT ALL

   Explanation:

4. As a consequence of the discussion, have you gained any new insights or new and useful information and understanding?

   A GREAT DEAL   SOME   VERY LITTLE

   Explanation:

5. Were you given opportunities to express your opinions and material?

   OFTEN   OCCASIONALLY   INFREQUENTLY

   Explanation:

6. Would you suggest any changes in the leadership of the discussion?

   MANY   A FEW   NONE AT ALL

   Explanation:

7. Which of the following changes would benefit the group? (Check as many as you wish.)

   _____ a. Better statement of questions to be explored.
   _____ b. Better individual preparation.
   _____ c. More responsible leadership.
   _____ d. More carefully planned agenda.
   _____ e. More democratic leadership.
   _____ f. More consideration for members of the group.
   _____ g. A greater sharing of leadership responsibilities.
   _____ h. A different procedure.
   _____ i. A friendlier atmosphere.
   _____ j. Consideration of different topics for discussion.
   _____ k. A more valid approach to discussion.
   _____ l. A change in the behavior of the instructor.

   Explanation:

Group Reaction Sheet

Group:

Date:

(Please check the point on each scale that represents your considered opinion. If you wish to clarify or explain your decision, please do so briefly in the space indicated by "Explanation". Do not sign your name.)

1. Are you satisfied with the conclusions (if any) reached in the discussion?

    VERY   MODERATELY   NOT AT ALL

    Explanation:

2. Were the attitudes of your fellow discussants conducive to cooperative action?

    VERY   MODERATELY   NOT AT ALL

    Explanation:

3. Did the group adopt and follow an orderly or systematic approach toward the solving of the problem confronting it?

    TOO MUCH SO   VERY MUCH SO   SOMEWHAT   NOT AT ALL

    Explanation:

4. As a consequence of the discussion, have you gained any new insights or new and useful information and understanding?

    A GREAT DEAL   SOME   VERY LITTLE

    Explanation:

5. Were you given opportunities to express your opinions and material?

    OFTEN   OCCASIONALLY   INFREQUENTLY

    Explanation:

6. Would you suggest any changes in the leadership of the discussion?

    MANY   A FEW   NONE AT ALL

    Explanation:

7. Which of the following changes would benefit the group? (Check as many as you wish.)

    _____ a. Better statement of questions to be explored.
    _____ b. Better individual preparation.
    _____ c. More responsible leadership.
    _____ d. More carefully planned agenda.
    _____ e. More democratic leadership.
    _____ f. More consideration for members of the group.
    _____ g. A greater sharing of leadership responsibilities.
    _____ h. A different procedure.
    _____ i. A friendlier atmosphere.
    _____ j. Consideration of different topics for discussion.
    _____ k. A more valid approach to discussion.
    _____ l. A change in the behavior of the instructor.

    Explanation:

Group Reaction Sheet

Group:
Date:

(Please check the point on each scale that represents your considered opinion. If you wish to clarify or explain your decision, please do so briefly in the space indicated by "Explanation". Do not sign your name.)

1. Are you satisfied with the conclusions (if any) reached in the discussion?

    VERY   MODERATELY   NOT AT ALL

    Explanation:

---

2. Were the attitudes of your fellow discussants conducive to cooperative action?

    VERY   MODERATELY   NOT AT ALL

    Explanation:

---

3. Did the group adopt and follow an orderly or systematic approach toward the solving of the problem confronting it?

    TOO MUCH SO   VERY MUCH SO   SOMEWHAT   NOT AT ALL

    Explanation:

---

4. As a consequence of the discussion, have you gained any new insights or new and useful information and understanding?

    A GREAT DEAL   SOME   VERY LITTLE

    Explanation:

---

5. Were you given opportunities to express your opinions and material?

    OFTEN   OCCASIONALLY   INFREQUENTLY

    Explanation:

---

6. Would you suggest any changes in the leadership of the discussion?

    MANY   A FEW   NONE AT ALL

    Explanation:

---

7. Which of the following changes would benefit the group? (Check as many as you wish.)

    _____ a. Better statement of questions to be explored.
    _____ b. Better individual preparation.
    _____ c. More responsible leadership.
    _____ d. More carefully planned agenda.
    _____ e. More democratic leadership.
    _____ f. More consideration for members of the group.
    _____ g. A greater sharing of leadership responsibilities.
    _____ h. A different procedure.
    _____ i. A friendlier atmosphere.
    _____ j. Consideration of different topics for discussion.
    _____ k. A more valid approach to discussion.
    _____ l. A change in the behavior of the instructor.

    Explanation:

Group Reaction Sheet

Group:

Date:

(Please check the point on each scale that represents your considered opinion. If you wish to clarify or explain your decision, please do so briefly in the space indicated by "Explanation". Do not sign your name.)

1. Are you satisfied with the conclusions (if any) reached in the discussion?

    VERY   MODERATELY   NOT AT ALL

    Explanation:

2. Were the attitudes of your fellow discussants conducive to cooperative action?

    VERY   MODERATELY   NOT AT ALL

    Explanation:

3. Did the group adopt and follow an orderly or systematic approach toward the solving of the problem confronting it?

    TOO MUCH SO   VERY MUCH SO   SOMEWHAT   NOT AT ALL

    Explanation:

4. As a consequence of the discussion, have you gained any new insights or new and useful information and understanding?

    A GREAT DEAL   SOME   VERY LITTLE

    Explanation:

5. Were you given opportunities to express your opinions and material?

    OFTEN   OCCASIONALLY   INFREQUENTLY

    Explanation:

6. Would you suggest any changes in the leadership of the discussion?

    MANY   A FEW   NONE AT ALL

    Explanation:

7. Which of the following changes would benefit the group? (Check as many as you wish.)
    _____ a. Better statement of questions to be explored.
    _____ b. Better individual preparation.
    _____ c. More responsible leadership.
    _____ d. More carefully planned agenda.
    _____ e. More democratic leadership.
    _____ f. More consideration for members of the group.
    _____ g. A greater sharing of leadership responsibilities.
    _____ h. A different procedure.
    _____ i. A friendlier atmosphere.
    _____ j. Consideration of different topics for discussion.
    _____ k. A more valid approach to discussion.
    _____ l. A change in the behavior of the instructor.

    Explanation:

D. Filming Your Own Photosituations

At the final meeting of our classes, we usually request that the students indicate to us how the course might have been taught in order to increase its value. Until we accepted the suggestion, the following was repeated each term: "Why not waive the reliance upon ordinary testing methods and put us in a situation where our knowledge and creativity are more fully examined? Why not require, in place of a written quiz, descriptions of five situations which could be filmed, and the still picture execution, the photosituation, of at least one of these 'scenarios'? Then in a final oral or written situation, the class would try its analytical and perceptive powers on its own creations. You could grade us on how good the descriptions and the still pictures are."

Such procedures would not only produce new incidents for discussion but would also provide a good technique for clarifying, through photography, case studies and role-playing situations.

Here are some suggestions for filming such photosituations if you, like us, find the suggestion intriguing and an invitation to learning.

1. Try to picture the situation in your mind. A rough pencil sketch aids in composition.
2. Work with a minimum number of persons. Organization becomes difficult with many people to consider.
3. Do not depend on circumstance. Stage what you want and tell your subjects what you plan to do. For this purpose, they are actors.
4. Get all your props ready before your subjects come on the scene.
5. Emphasize the factors, or clues, you are trying to present by exaggeration or position. (Example. In the picture where the time of day is important, the clock is at the center of attention.)
6. Use a flash attachment on your camera. Available light photography may be more aesthetic but the flash makes the highlights stand out more dramatically.
7. Do not wait until you have an expensive camera. One of the popular makes which sells for twelve or fifteen dollars will produce quality sufficient for class work.
8. Consider the making of a slide for projection. The common 2" x 2" color slide, or a black-and-white made from a negative, or a black-and-white made from a positive film may be acceptable.

A Reminder

The frozen situations portrayed in the following pages have been set up with four pictures to each section involved. In selecting categories for grouping of the pictures, we picked out what seemed to us to be six of the most significant issues faced by teachers: (1) teacher ethics, (2) student motivation, (3) situation control, (4) classroom atmosphere, (5) faculty relationships, and (6) the school and the community. Our pictures begin with the

34

matter of teacher ethics. However, there is no particular reason for taking them in any particular sequence. We put them in the sequence found simply because it seemed convenient and, perhaps, because it began with an emphasis on a more internalized issue, then moved to issues concerned with teacher handling of students, and thence to relationships with co-workers and the community setting or areas outside the immediate teacher-pupil relationship. We recognize that one picture might contain within it material for discussion of more than one area. But we selected pictures for each area which we felt would help stimulate sound thinking concerning that specific area of issues.

Teachers' Ethics

"How often, knowing what is right, I do wrong!" Benjamin Franklin is reported to have said. And what distinguished company he has had throughout the ages! Meanwhile, most of us proclaim our allegiance to various codes of behavior or ethical standards regardless of our behavior.

We are, of course, not arguing against the adoption of ethical standards or codes of ethics for and by teachers. Whether in education, medicine, or politics, such codes can indicate the beliefs we treasure and the goals to which we aspire. And they can furnish the standards against which relevant action may be measured or judged. For pedagogical purposes they seem to be indispensable. But, we must remember, ethical considerations seldom appear singly and indivisibly--in the classroom or in the community. They are woven together, usually in subtle fashion, with a multiplicity of other elements: motives, standards, and human interests. Therefore the application of a particular course of action apparently sanctioned by adherence to a particular code of ethics must be preceded by considerable perception and reflection.

To illustrate the multiplicity of difficulties inherent in such adherence, let us look at Picture 3. A viewer might conclude from a cursory examination of the action frozen by the camera that the youngster in the foreground is simply receiving the wages of impartial justice. This conclusion might follow from the reading of the "Code of Ethics for Teachers" adopted in 1963 by the National Education Association. But another viewer might see an entirely different problem, one primarily involving the methods and consequences of discipline in the classroom. Still another viewer might see only the emotional consequences which the teacher and the students might experience. Actually, can we outlaw any projected impressions before advancing toward understanding? Probably not! But we must point out that there are some common principles--principles that should evolve during discussion.

Now, in preparation for class discussion and with the multiplicity of ethical factors in mind, let us examine Pictures 1, 2, 3, and 4 and fill out the questions which follow.

picture 1

picture 1

1.   Delineate the main ethical problem which you see in this picture.

2.   In this, identify any undesirable behavior.

3.   Develop a hypothesis explaining why this problem has occurred or is occurring.

picture 1

4. What principle or fundamental understanding about human behavior is your hypothesis built upon?

5. What evidence can you show to support the hypothesis? (Indicate any clues you see and establish a relationship between each and the hypothesis.)

6.   Suggest what can be done to modify the undesirable behavior identified in line with your hypothesis and the stated generalization.

picture 2

picture 2

1. Delineate the main ethical problem which you see in this picture.

2.   In this, identify any undesirable behavior.

3.   Form a hypothesis explaining why this problem has occurred or is occurring?

picture 2

4. Indicate the principle of behavior to which the hypothesis is related.

5. What evidence can you show to support the hypothesis? (Indicate any clues you see and establish a relationship between each and the hypothesis.)

6. Suggest what can be done to modify the undesirable behavior identified in line with your hypothesis and the stated generalization.

picture 3

picture 3

1. Indicate how many ethical problems you see in this picture and describe them.

2.   In this picture, identify any undesirable behavior.

3. Form a hypothesis explaining why this problem has occurred or is occurring.

picture 3

4. Indicate the principle of behavior to which the hypothesis is related.

5. What evidence can you show to support the hypothesis? (Indicate any clues you see and establish a relationship between each and the hypothesis.)

6. Suggest what can be done to modify the undesirable behavior identified in line with your hypothesis and the stated generalization.

picture 4

picture 4

1. Delineate the main ethical problem which you see in this picture.

2. In this picture, identify any undesirable behavior.

picture 4

3. Form a hypothesis explaining why this problem has occurred or is occurring?

picture 4

4. Indicate the principle of behavior to which the hypothesis is related.

picture 4

5. What evidence can you show to support the hypothesis? (Indicate any clues you see and establish a relationship between each and the hypothesis.)

picture 4

6. Suggest what can be done to modify the undesirable behavior identified in line with your hypothesis and the stated generalization.

Student Motivation

Each student is an individual and the depth and breadth of his learning depend upon the personal stimulation and support he receives. So goes one of the cardinal principles advocated for teachers. Recognition and acceptance of this principle is a persistent challenge facing teachers, potential teachers, and their employers. Yet neither acceptance nor recognition of the challenge may clarify for the teacher the complexity of demands and the internal confusion which may come as he attempts to apply the principle. Student motivation, when dealing with individuals or when involving a class of 25 to 30 students, becomes a complex matter of determining need, experimenting, confessing error, and searching for new perspectives and new approaches.

In Pictures 5, 6, 7, and 8 are portrayed a number of situations which might confront you. They depict differing evidences of motivation, ranging from possible apathy to belligerence. Each situation appears to give focus to a certain aspect of motivation, yet there may be common elements involved.

The accompanying questions are raised to help the individual develop a keener perspective towards student motivation. The questions are worded to give the student opportunity to compare his perspective with that of others while acquiring some feeling for the likely consequences of differing viewpoints and the ways of dealing with them.

picture 5

picture 5

1. What is the basic motivational issue depicted in this picture? What, if anything, is wrong in this picture?

picture 5

2. If there is a problem, what is the teacher's responsibility?

picture 5

3.   What approaches might the teacher use to meet this responsibility?

picture 5

4.   What consequences can you see might come from the differing ways of meeting this responsibility?

picture 5

5.   What preventive measures might be taken to avoid this situation in a classroom?

71

picture 6

picture 6

1.   What problem, if any, do you see in this picture?

73

2.   If there is a problem, how is this problem related to motivation of a
     student ?

picture 6

3.   What seems to be the present approach to the problem? (What clues give you such an idea?)

picture 6

4.   What better approaches to the issue might be used?

picture 7

1. Do you see any motivational problems in this picture? If so, what are the clues which suggest them to you?

picture 7

2.   What appears to be the present pattern for handling the problems?

picture 7

3. What else might need to be done to motivate the student?

4.   What other approaches might a teacher use in dealing with the type of motivation problems reflected in this picture?

picture 8

1.   What is going on in the picture?

picture 8

2.   Assuming there is a motivational problem involved, what do you think
it would be? (What gives you the clues?)

picture 8

3. What is being done about it? (What likely results are to be expected?)

4. What else might be done?

Situational Control

Situations in which several facets of teaching demands are in play at one time often bedevil the teacher. Handling lesson presentation, classroom management, individual motivation, and other issues as separate items allows opportunity for rational thought and action; but when immediate situations arise in which classroom discipline gets mixed up with concern for the welfare of a certain child and with a teacher's own emotional or ethical concerns, it becomes easy to make mistakes.

Pictures 9, 10, 11, and 12 portray four such situations. In each a teacher's concern for the welfare of an individual, for personal or school ethics, for the well-being of daily school operation, or other considerations may be seen. The challenge existing for teachers is at least twofold: (1) to determine how much emphasis to give to each aspect of the situation, and (2) to understand the aspects toward which he may be drawn emotionally and the consequences of such emotional involvement.

In preparation for the discussion of these pictures please answer the accompanying questions.

picture 9

1. What is the teacher's biggest problem here?

picture 9

2. What courses of action are available to the teacher in the situation?

picture 9

3.   What are the likely consequences of each course of action?

91

4.   Which of these approaches do you favor? Why?

picture 10

picture 10

1. What is happening in this scene? Indicate the clues which support your conclusion.

picture 10

2. What can the teacher do in this situation?

picture 10

3.   What are the likely consequences of each course of action?

picture 10

4.   How can situations like this be avoided?

picture 11

1.   What is out of control in this situation?

picture 11

2.   What can the teacher do in the situation?

3.   What are the likely consequences of differing actions?

4.   How can such situations be avoided?

picture 12

picture 12

1.   What should the teacher's major concern be in this situation?

picture 12

2. What are the courses of action available in the situation? What are their likely consequences?

picture 12

3. Suppose one did make an error in handling such a situation, what con-
    siderations might reduce the likelihood of error in future situations?

Classroom Atmosphere

A teacher spends about a thousand hours a year in the classroom. If only for his peace of mind, it is vital that he create in that classroom an atmosphere conducive to effective teaching. It is equally vital that his pupils enjoy an atmosphere beneficial to their learning and their mental health. However, experience echoes the old "saw" that intentions and actions are not always cut from the same cloth. Teachers are only human, despite the expectations of a segment of the American public. In human fashion, they make mistakes with varied effects upon their own behavior as well as upon the behavior and learning of their pupils.

In Pictures 13, 14, 15, and 16 we may witness a variety of situations involving at least one principle commonly accepted as a basis for establishing or maintaining good classroom atmosphere. The accompanying questions ask you to identify these principles and consider the implications surrounding their application.

picture 13

picture 13

1.   What appears to be happening in this situation? What clues support your observation?

picture 13

2. What specific principles of classroom atmosphere are being demon-
    strated or violated?

110

3. If you were the teacher involved in the situation, what changes, if any, would you attempt to initiate in order to improve the situation?

picture 13

4. Assuming that you have entered the picture at this precise time, how would you proceed to implement these changes?

picture 14

picture 14

1.   What appears to be happening in this situation? What clues support your observation?

picture 14

2. What specific principles of classroom atmosphere are being demon-
    strated or violated?

picture 14

3. If you were the teacher involved in the situation, what changes, if any, would you attempt to initiate in order to improve the situation?

picture 14

4. Assuming you are the principal and you enter the picture at this precise time, what would you do?

picture 15

picture 15

1. What appears to be happening in this situation? What clues support your observation?

picture 15

2. What specific principles of classroom atmosphere are being demonstrated or violated?

picture 15

3. If you were the teacher involved in the situation, what changes, if any, would you attempt to initiate in order to improve the situation?

picture 15

4. Assuming that you have entered the picture at this precise time, how would you proceed to implement these changes?

picture 16

123

1.   What appears to be happening in this situation? What clues support your observation?

picture 16

2. What specific principles of classroom atmosphere are being demon-
    strated or violated?

picture 16

3. If you were the teacher involved in the situation, what changes, if any, would you attempt to initiate in order to improve the situation?

4.   Assuming that you have entered the picture at this precise time, how
     would you proceed to implement these changes?

Faculty Relationships

It seems to be characteristic of teachers that they react warmly to their fellows. In most schools, for example, the new teacher is assured of a cordial reception and the opportunity to make friends among his colleagues. In most faculty groups there is a general recognition that individual contributions of sensitive understanding and sincere cooperation are necessary to establish high morale and maintain a good educational program.

But within the school family, as in other arenas of human conduct, misunderstanding and the absence of kindness may complicate the relationships of teacher with teacher or teacher with administrator. The well intentioned giving of advice by an older to a younger teacher may avoid difficulty, or, it may, under certain circumstances, augment difficulty. The summons to a principal's office may resolve a personal problem, or it may, depending upon the situation, magnify the problem.

In Pictures 17, 18, 19, and 20 we have captured some of the situations which have faced us in a variety of schools. Examine each picture closely and then turn to the accompanying questions.

picture 17

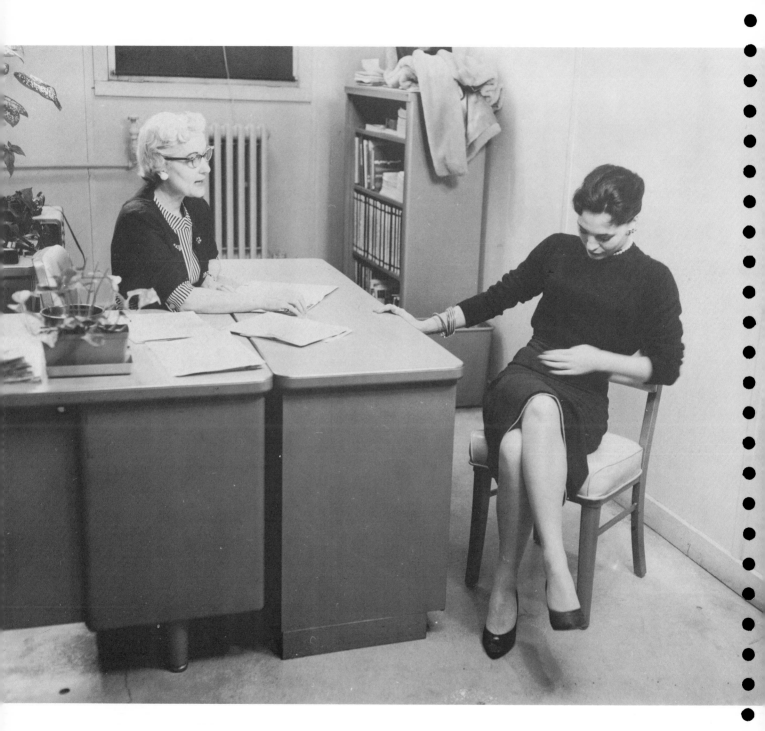

picture 17

1. What issues or issue involving faculty relationships appear (s) to be in-
    volved? What clues indicate the issue?

picture 17

2.   What aspect of good human relations is missing or is illustrated in the situation?

picture 17

3.   What might be a likely conclusion if the situation as you interpret it is allowed to develop?

picture 17

4. How might good faculty relationships be re-established after a breakdown has occurred?

picture 18

picture 18

1. What issues or issue involving faculty relationships appear (s) to be in-
    volved?   What clues indicate the issue?

picture 18

2. What aspect of good human relations is missing or is illustrated in the situation?

picture 18

3. What might be a likely conclusion if the situation as you interpret it is allowed to develop?

137

4. In the problem identified, what would you do in support of or in criticism
    of the teacher under question?

picture 19

picture 19

1. What issues or issue involving faculty relationships appear (s) to be involved? What clues indicate the issue?

picture 19

2.   What aspect of good human relations is missing or is illustrated in the situation?

picture 19

3. What might be a likely conclusion if the situation as you interpret it is allowed to develop?

picture 19

4. How might good faculty relationships be re-established after the break-down has occurred?

143

picture 20

1. What issues or issue involving faculty relationships appear (s) to be involved? What clues indicate the issue?

picture 20

2. What aspect of good human relations is missing or is illustrated in the situation?

picture 20

3.   What might be a likely conclusion if the situation as you interpret it is allowed to develop?

picture 20

4. How might good faculty relationships be re-established after the break-down has occurred?

School and Community

When an individual accepts a teaching position in a school, he becomes more than a teacher. He becomes a part of a public institution and, therefore, in one sense, public property. Rightly or wrongly, the citizenry feels it has the right to define the role played by its servants and to determine the behavioral limits within which these servants may operate. It even believes that the time, energy, and other resources of public servants should be available for any or all efforts dealing with community well-being.

In the face of such expectations, the teacher may be amazed by the "fish bowl" nature of his life, the restrictions which may be imposed, or the demands made upon him. But, on the other hand, in some communities he may be disturbed by the apparent apathy of the public toward his role or public function.

Regardless of his individual situation, these matters become increasingly pertinent for the teacher. He needs sensitivity to perceive adequately the role he is expected to play. He needs a philosophy capable of coping with social change, a philosophy that will enable him to modify the situation as well as adapt to it.

The following pictures (21, 22, 23, and 24) portray certain aspects of the problems encountered by the teacher as he enters the school-community area. The accompanying questions may activate your perception and point up your analysis as you scrutinize the situations.

picture 21

picture 21

1. What is the major issue of school or teacher-community relationships
    in this situation?

picture 21

2. What other issues may be present?

picture 21

3.   Are the issues reconcilable? If so, how; if not, why?

picture 22

picture 22

1. What is the major issue of school or teacher-community relationships in this situation?

picture 22

2.   What other issues may be present?

picture 22

3.   Are the issues reconcilable? If so, how; if not, why?

157

picture 23

1. What problem of school or teacher-community relationship is indicated in this picture?

picture 23

2.   What other issues may be present?

picture 23

3. How can these issues be brought to the attention of the community?

picture 23

4. What are the teacher's responsibilities in problems like these?

picture 24

picture 24

1. What is the major issue of school or teacher-community relationship in this situation?

picture 24

2.   What other issues may be present?

picture 24

3. What can be done about this problem?

166

"You never know what is enough unless

you know what is more than enough. "

William Blake, <u>The Marriage of Heaven and Hell</u>.